BLACKBERRY FARM

THE ADVENTURES OF WALTER

Jane Pilgrim

This edition first published in the United Kingdom in 1999 by
Brockhampton Press
20 Bloomsbury Street
London WC1B 3QA
a member of the Hodder Headline PLC Group

Designed and Produced for Brockhampton Press by
Open Door Limited
80 High Street, Colsterworth, Lincolnshire, NG33 5JA

Illustrator: F. Stocks May
Colour separation: GA Graphics Stamford

Title: BLACKBERRY FARM, The Adventures of Walter
ISBN: 1-84186-005-0

THE ADVENTURES OF WALTER

Jane Pilgrim

Illustrated by F. Stocks May

BROCKHAMPTON PRESS

Walter was a large white duck who lived at Blackberry Farm. He had a strong yellow beak, and he always wore a woollen scarf around his neck, because he had been hatched out on a windy day and his mother had been afraid that he would catch cold.

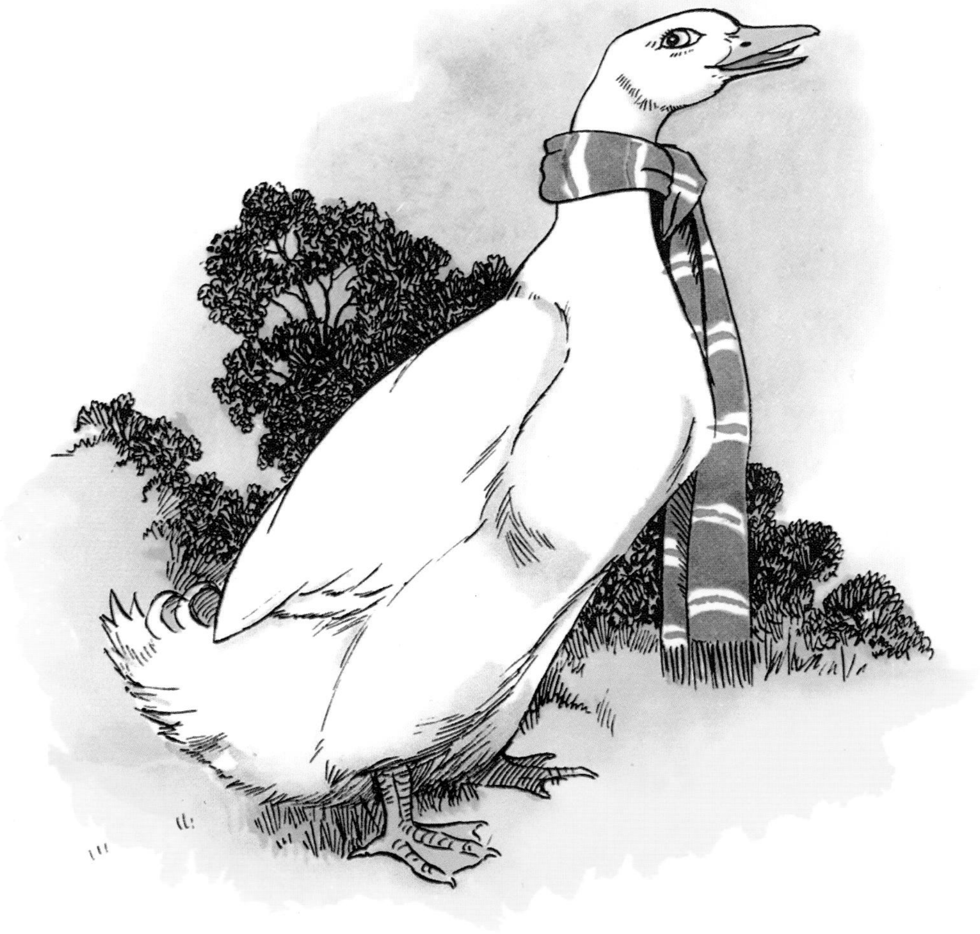

Every day Walter went down to
the little pond beyond the farm to
see what he could find in the
water. "There might be something
really tasty here one day," he
explained to his friend Mother
Hen, when she found him upside
down in the pond with only his
tail showing.

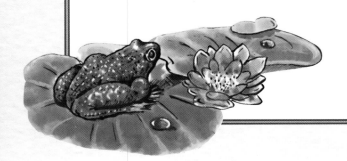

But Walter began to get tired of the pond. He never did find anything tasty there. He thought he would like a change. "Tell me," he asked Rusty the Sheep Dog, "where I can find some new exciting water. I'm tired of this dull old pond." So Rusty told him about the little river that flowed through the village and on to the fields beyond.

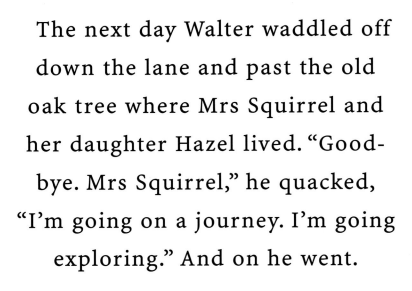

The next day Walter waddled off down the lane and past the old oak tree where Mrs Squirrel and her daughter Hazel lived. "Good-bye. Mrs Squirrel," he quacked, "I'm going on a journey. I'm going exploring." And on he went.

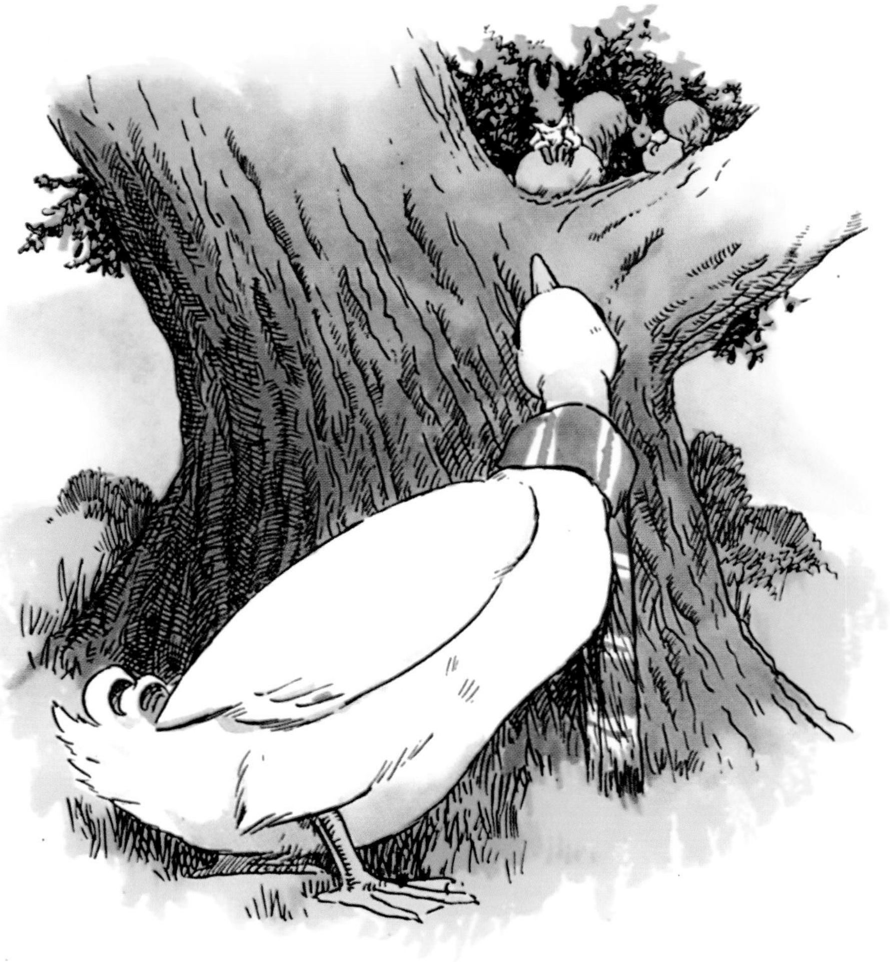

Sure enough, at the end of the lane was a little bridge, and under the bridge a little river. Walter was delighted, and in a minute he was sailing away towards the village. "This is life," he thought. "This is better than my dull old pond."

And he swam on.

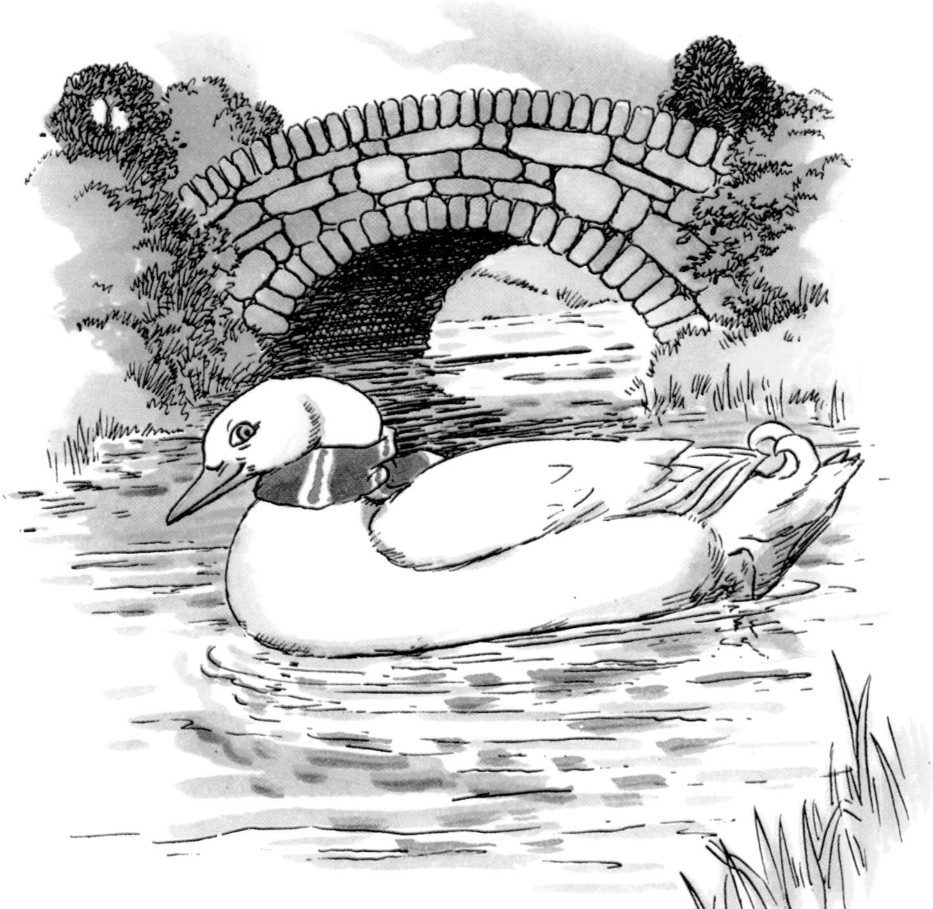

When he reached the village, Walter stopped and looked around. An old lady threw him a crust. He quacked his thanks and sailed on. "This is good," he thought. "This is better than my dull old pond." And on he went.

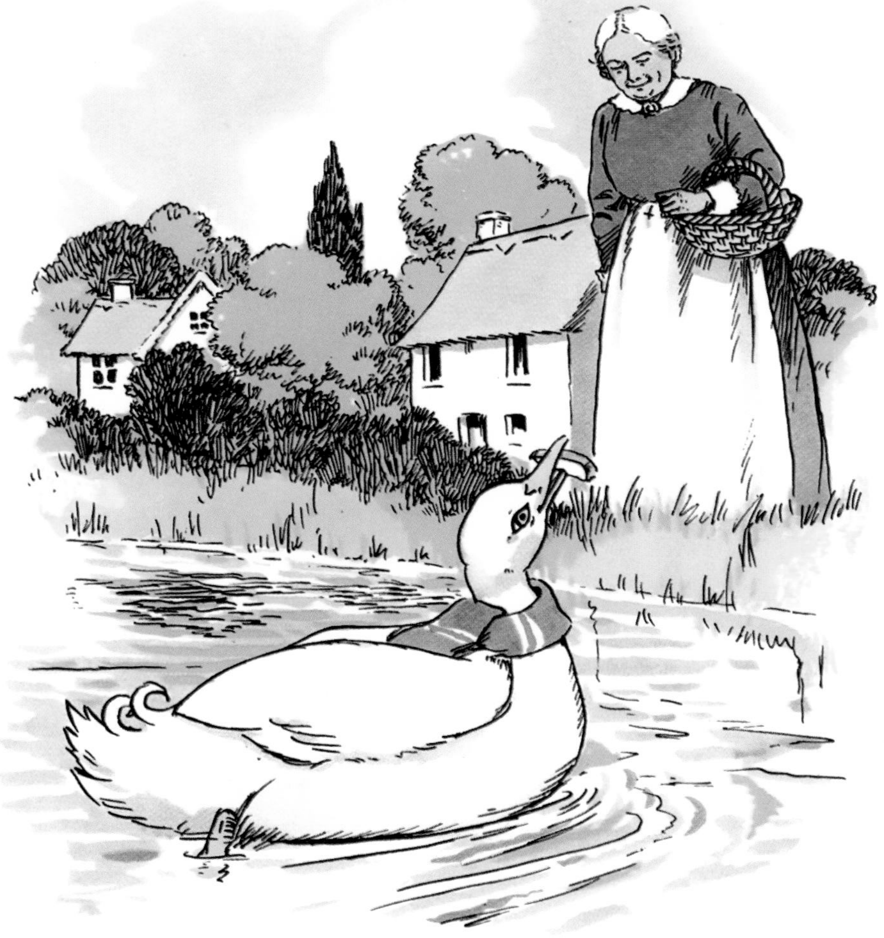

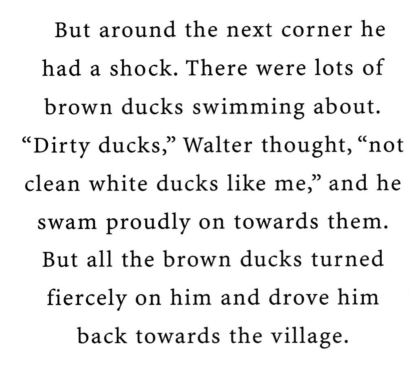

But around the next corner he had a shock. There were lots of brown ducks swimming about. "Dirty ducks," Walter thought, "not clean white ducks like me," and he swam proudly on towards them. But all the brown ducks turned fiercely on him and drove him back towards the village.

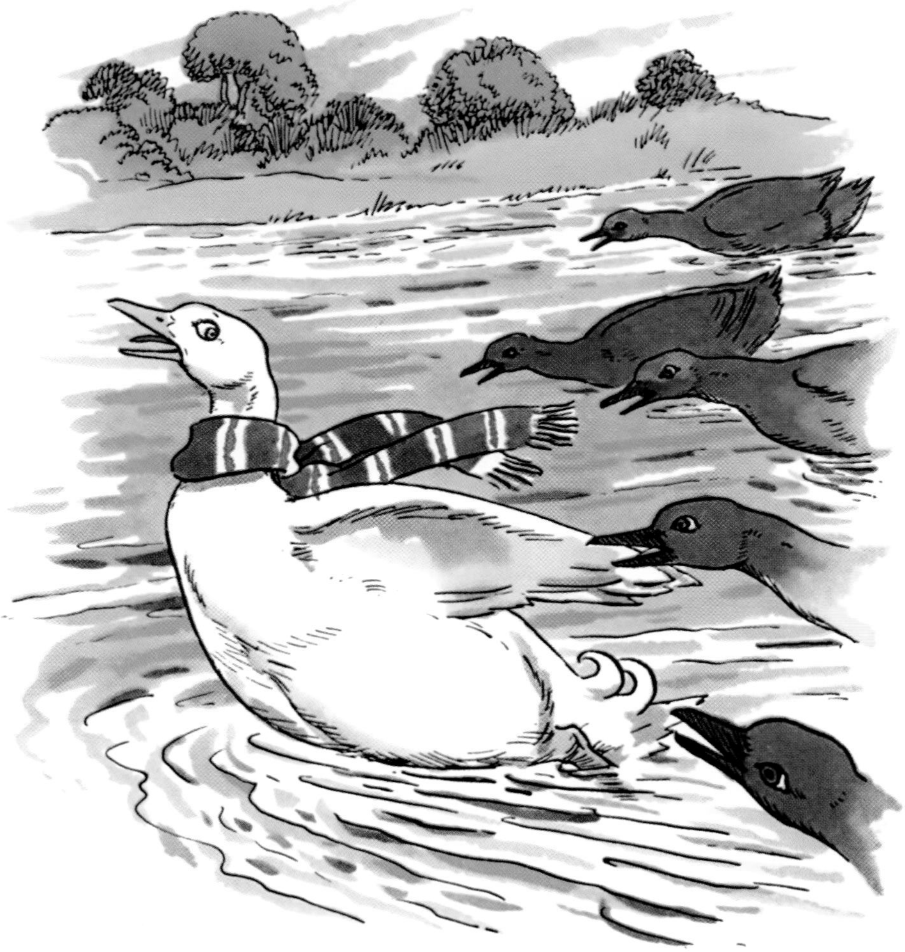

"Oh dear!" sighed Walter. "Now I won't be able to see those nice green fields." And he decided to climb the bank and walk along the path. So he waddled along, humming a tune to himself. Then suddenly he saw a large black dog asleep across his path.

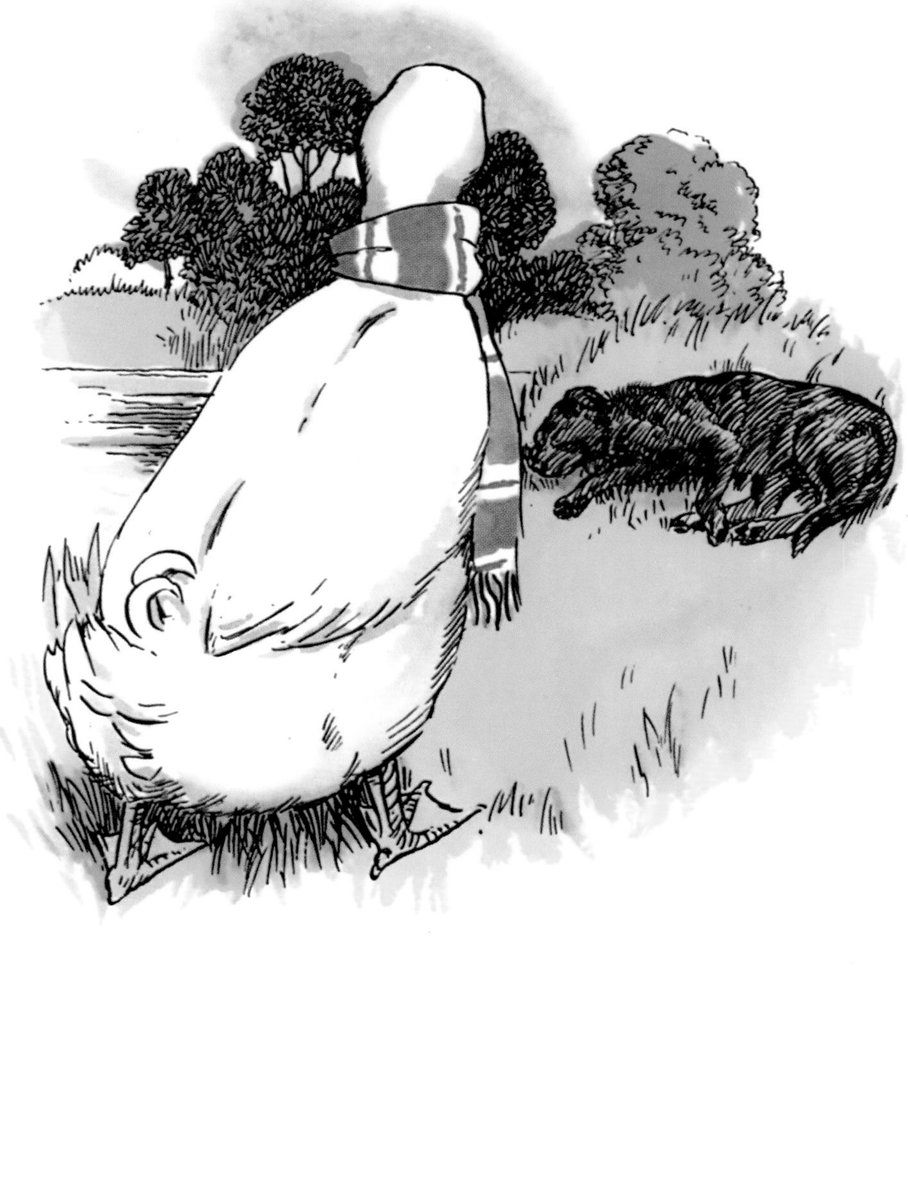

Walter was alarmed. The only
dog he knew was Rusty the Sheep
Dog, and he was a friendly dog.
But he had heard that some dogs
like to chase ducks. "I must creep
round him very carefully," he
thought, "without waking him up.
Then I shall be all right." And he
began to creep very carefully.

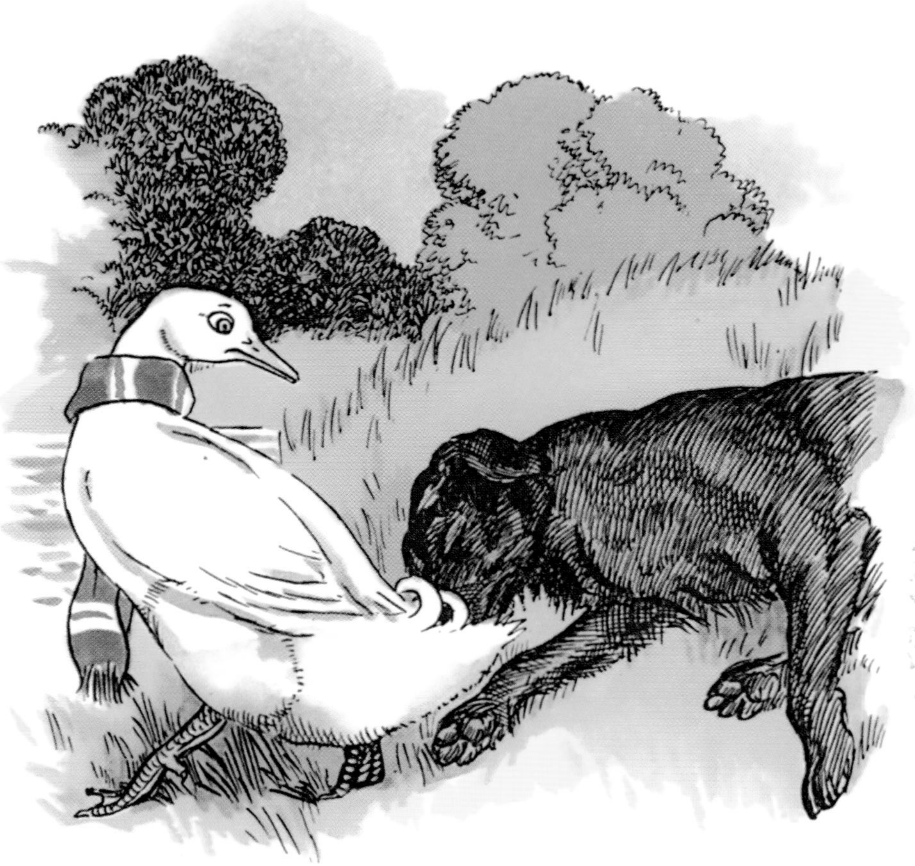

And he did creep very carefully,
but one feather from his wing-tip
must have tickled the Black Dog's
nose, because he suddenly opened
his eyes and saw Walter.

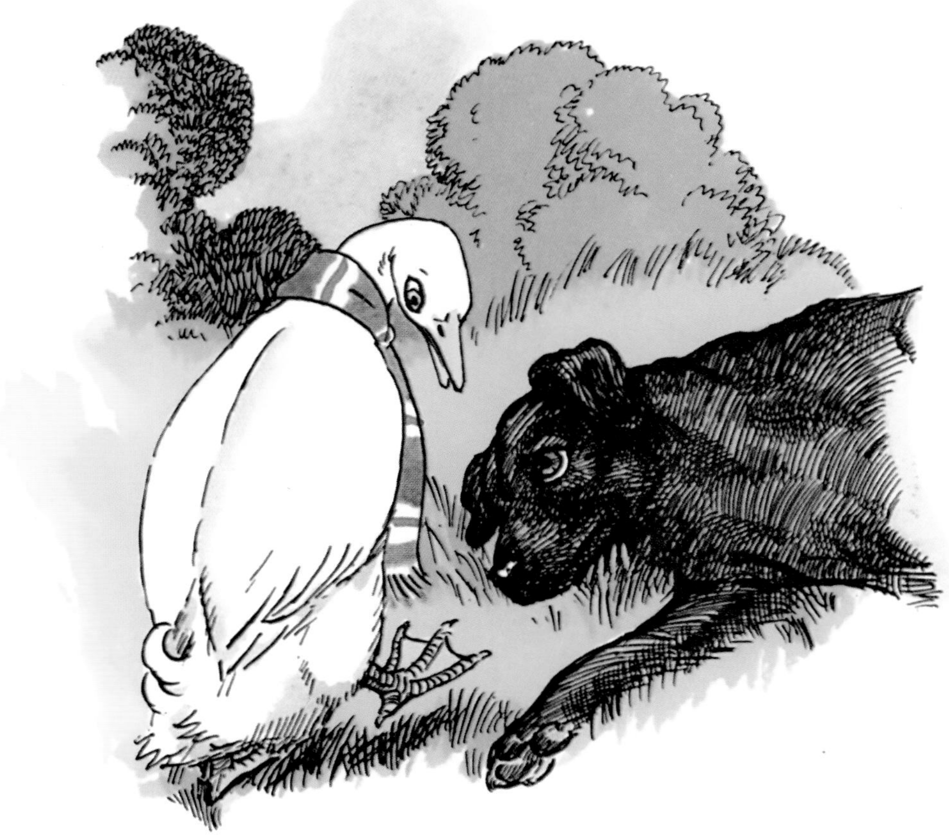

Now, the Black Dog did not know that it was Walter Duck from Blackberry Farm. He thought Walter was just a lost white duck and that it was his duty to catch lost white ducks and take them home. So, in a second, he had lifted Walter up and was carrying him carefully in his mouth down the path towards the village. How Walter quacked and wriggled! He wasn't hurt, but he was very frightened. When would he see his dear little pond again?

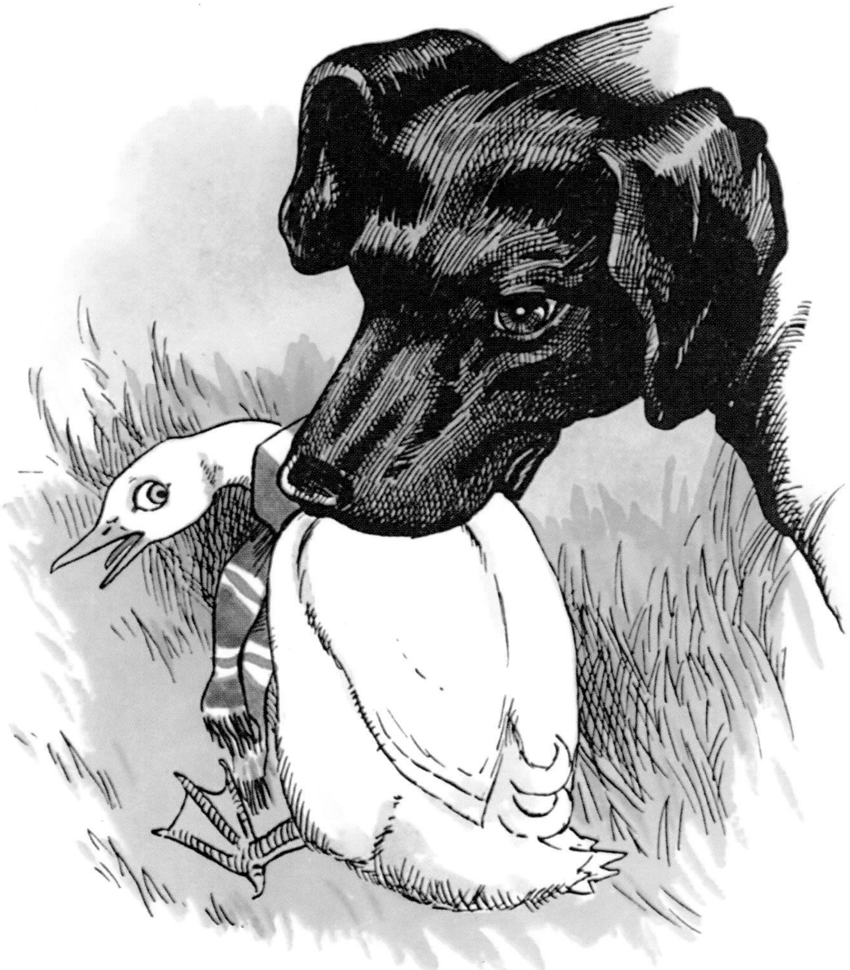

Two large tears rolled down his beak. It was then that Rusty met them. "Whatever are you doing with our Walter?" he asked the Black Dog, and the Black Dog had to put Walter down before he could answer. Walter did not wait to hear the answer. He was off down the bank and into the river, swimming as fast as he could away from the village, and home to Blackberry Farm.

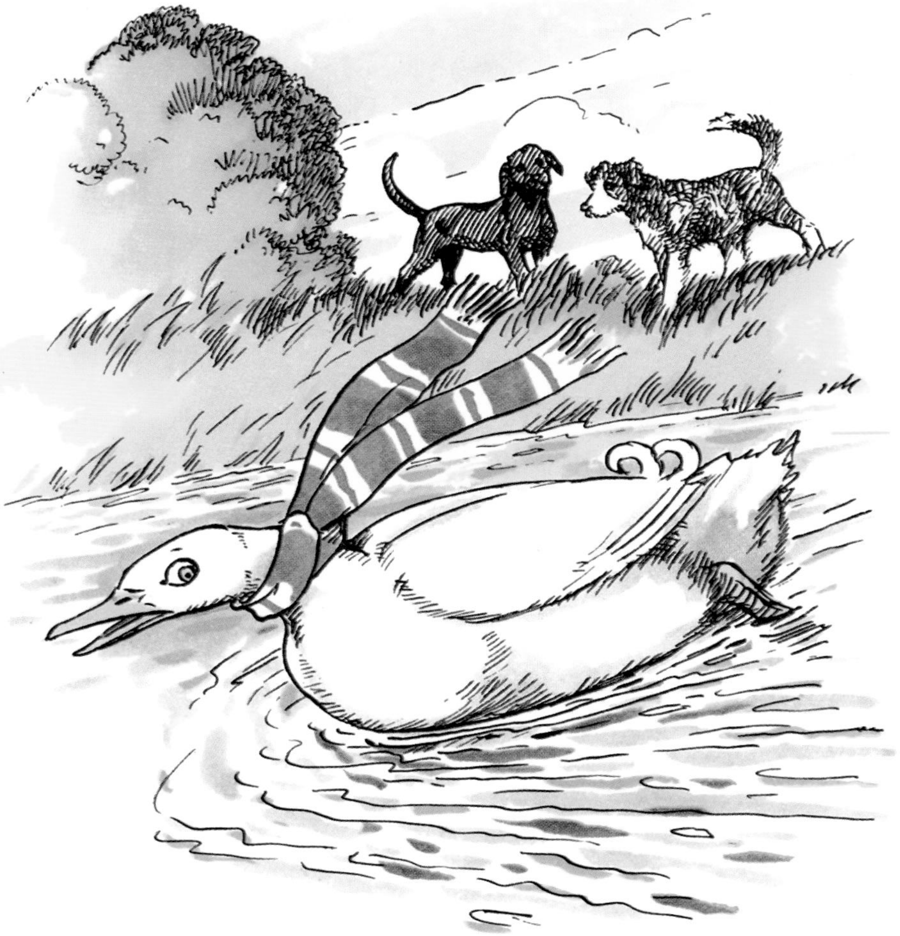

Rusty found him waddling down
the lane past the old oak tree
where Mrs Squirrel lived. "It's all
right, Walter," he told him. "That
Black Dog would not have hurt
you. He's a friend of mine. But
next time you go exploring, I
think you had better come with
me, and I will look after you."

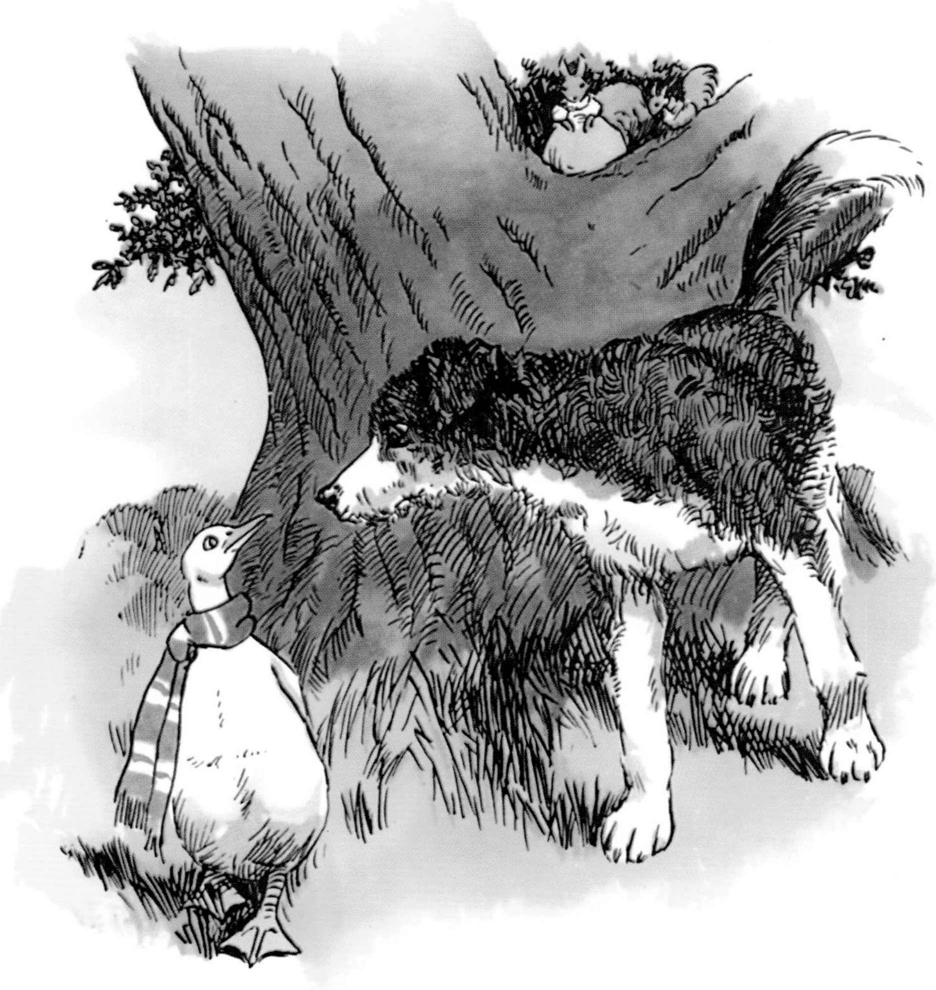

Walter was very glad to get home to his little pond again, and to find Mother Hen waiting for him. "The world is a very exciting place," he told her. "But I like Blackberry Farm best. I think I shall stay here for a long time." And he waddled happily into his own dull muddy water.

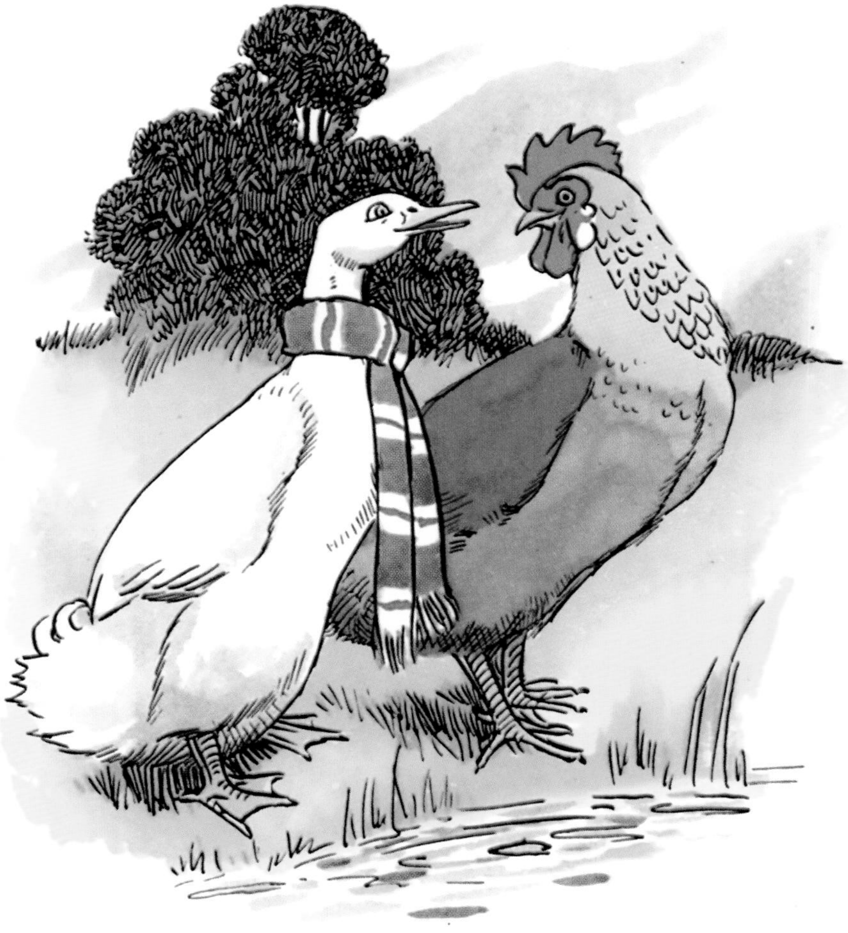

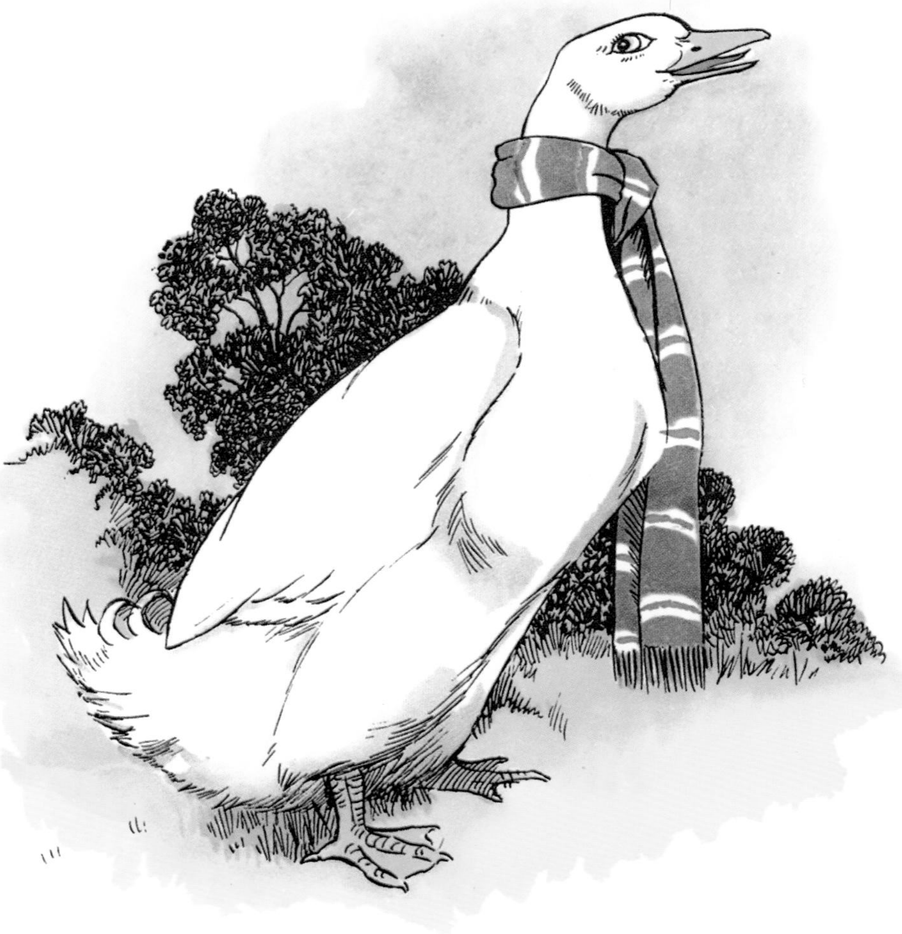